Figure 8 Animals
Creative Ideas Across the Curriculum

by
Troy W. Cole

illustrated by Troy W. Cole and June Kern Weber

Cover by Tom Sjoerdsma

Quality Books 6-8-93 12.45

Copyright © 1993, Good Apple

ISBN No. 0-86653-721-X

Printing No. 987654321

Good Apple
1204 Buchanan St., Box 299
Carthage, IL 62321-0299

S I M O N & S C H U S T E R   *A Paramount Communications Company*

Acknowledgments

This book was written because of these
very special people.

My mentor who believes in me,
my special friend
Bob Stanish.

A super teacher and educator,
my wife, my companion, my editor,
the mother of our sons
and my very best friend
Betty J. Cole.

This book is dedicated to my sons
Vance W. Cole
Kort E. Cole
Kade P. Cole

Foreword

For many years I have demonstrated figure 8 drawing in classrooms and at teacher workshops. As a result, I have had many requests to "write it up so we can use it in our own classrooms."

Here it is "written up." I hope you can use it.

Troy

Preface

Troy Cole orchestrates a beautiful blending of mind hemispheres. He provides words and figures and encourages us to diverge and extend them through transformations and adaptations in a fun and meaningful way. And he shows us how to see the interconnectiveness of things. But most importantly, he provides a step-by-step procedure by which children and adults can see, do, bond, adapt and extend concepts and information.

Children will love it, for they will transform the what is into what it might become. This, beyond anything else, builds and nurtures imagination and creative inventiveness. Parents will love it, for they will observe their child's excitement and involvement. Teachers will love it, for it will accommodate a whole mind approach to learning. And for thousands of teachers who await Troy Cole's popular two-page layout of "Minute Minders" in each issue of *Challenge* magazine, there is a bountiful and wonderful harvest of creative thinking, writing, feeling and thought-provoking challenges in this book.

Bob Stanish

Bob Stanish

GA1439

Table of Contents

Introduction

Many years ago, while teaching high school math, I discovered figure 8 drawing. The number eight, when written, seemed a perfect shape for drawing faces–two circles with a line in the middle. Anyone can make an 8. I have yet to meet the first child above the age of five who cannot, in some form or other, do figure 8 drawing.

Thousands of children have done figure 8 drawing. I know because I did it with them as a classroom teacher and as a consultant and administrator.

Some drawings I have seen are quite unique. Excellence appears unexpected, and the very best part is that no one can fail. Different, unique, but always with success.

I have also noticed that children who may have perceptual difficulties often appear as Picassos. Some of their drawings are very interesting indeed. Watch for, appreciate, and enjoy each child's unique talent.

GA1439

About This Book

This book introduces using a figure 8 to draw animal faces. It begins with a simple figure 8 and demonstrates how by adding eyes, nose, ears, mouth and other features a variety of animal faces are created. A demonstration of figure 8 drawing is very important in getting started.

This book is divided into units that go beyond drawing. Each unit contains student activities which integrate drawing with reading, writing, imagining, designing, inventing, creating and feeling. The activities may be reproduced and used for classroom instruction or each unit could become part of an interest center.

This book gives some basic information about animals. A brief informational reference is provided about the animals in each unit.

This book provides activities for a variety of learning styles and preferences. Students may choose activities that match their individual learning styles and preferences. Some of the activities are written as group projects; others can easily be adapted for group projects.

This book encourages teachers to be creative. Teachers should feel free to adapt activities for their students and redialogue instructions with age appropriate vocabulary. The skills developed in this book are applicable to many areas of the curriculum. Look for the opportunities for students to apply these skills.

Note: Creative problem solving, transforming and valuing are integral skills of this book. Several of the writing activities use morphological synthesis to encourage and enhance writing. Whole minded and whole language experiences are prevalent. Looking, thinking, choosing and doing as a teaching and learning method is emphasized.

GA1439

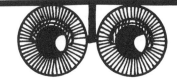

Getting

Started

with

Figure 8

Animals

GA1439

Getting Started

**It all starts with a
simple figure 8.**

**Face features are added.
The eyes, nose, mouth,
and ears are put in place.
A unique drawing is produced.**

**Share with others
and have fun!**

2

GA1439

Thinking About It

First draw a figure 8.

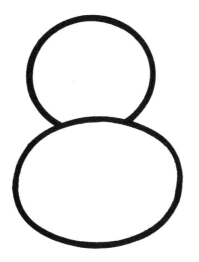

Think about an animal you would like to draw.

Would you like to draw
a cow?   a giraffe?
a horse?   an elephant?
a cat?   a pig?
a bird?   a rabbit?
a dog?   a deer?
or something else?
What? _____

To draw it, you must think about its face.
Big or little? Long or short?
What is the shape, size, and location of
the eyes, nose, mouth and ears?

Choose an animal you would like to draw.

On the 8 below think about where you would put the eyes, nose, mouth and ears.

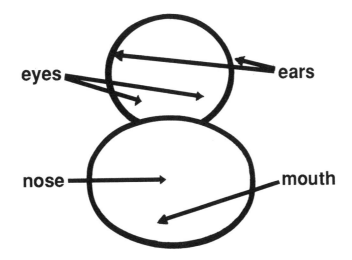

GA1439

Some cows I drew.

Now it is your turn.

4

Let's draw a cow.

A cow's face is big and long. Draw a big long 8.

A cow's eyes are big. Draw two big eyes just touching the line in the middle of the 8.

A cow's nose is long with two big nostrils. Draw two big nostrils at the bottom of the 8.

A cow's mouth is big. Draw a big smiley mouth under the two big nostrils.

A cow's ears are where? On the side of her head. Put a long, round, floppy ear on each side of her head.

Add some horns and maybe a neck.

You have drawn a cow!

GA1439

A Cow

Drawn by

_____

A Short Story About My Cow

_____

_____

_____

_____

_____

Cows

About Cows

Cows are members of the bovine family. In some cultures cows are sacred, in others a measure of wealth, and yet to others a major source of food and products.

As a group cows are called cattle. Cattle are the most useful of all animals. They provide dairy products and meat for food, hides for leather, hoofs for glue, bones for fertilizer, and horns for decorating things.

Cattle were domesticated in prehistoric time. From that time to the present time, breeding and improving cattle has been a very important effort. As a result, we have many different kinds of cattle.

In the bovine family we also find oxen, bison, buffalo, yaks and zebu. (I don't know what a zebu is. Do you?)

The Purple Cow
I never saw a purple cow
I never hope to see one.
But I can tell you, anyhow.
I'd rather see than be one.
Gelett Burgess

Think about—discuss—write about being different.

A Story About Prim

When I was a boy growing up on a farm in the Ozarks, we had a cow named Prim. She was very pretty for a cow and as tame and gentle as could be. She gave lots of milk, but she preferred to spend her time with people rather than cows. She liked to be petted.

When my brothers, sister or I were in sight, Prim would leave the other cattle and come romping across the pasture to us for attention. She would follow us around staying close and seemed always to be begging to be petted.

One day I decided that Prim was friendly enough to ride. I lifted my little sister onto Prim's back. Prim looked as if she enjoyed having Sis there. Then I hoisted brother Gary up. I am sure Prim smiled. She walked carefully beside me around the barnyard with the two riders on her back. Then I climbed aboard. Prim walked, then trotted, then walked again while the three of us, laughing and shouting, rode her all around.

It was about then that Mother came running from the house to see what all the shouting was about. When she saw the three of us all riding Prim, she almost fainted.

"Get off that cow! Do you all want to get killed?" she screamed.

"I don't want to see you kids near that cow again," she commanded as we slid off Prim's back.

Sis, Gary, and I tried never to let Mother see us near Prim again; we never got killed; nor, did we stop petting and riding Prim. But always out of the sight of Mother.

There were many pets on our farm: two dogs, a sheep named Johnny, a goat named Buster, and a horse named Ribbon, but Prim was our only pet cow. When my family left the farm, all the cattle were sold. All that is except Prim. She stayed. The family that bought our farm had agreed to let Prim live there for the rest of her life—which she did. Prim lived a long and attention-filled life as a pet cow on that farm in the hills of the Ozarks.

GA1439

This page is for thinking, writing, reading and drawing.

What I Know About Cows

My Little Cow Drawings

Finish this poem.

If I brought a cow to school, I know that I would break a rule.

_____

_____

What do you think would happen if every family had to keep a cow to have milk, butter and cheese?

Looking and Choosing

On the next four pages you will find a sampling of the different shapes and sizes you can use in figure 8 drawing. These are only samples. When you do figure 8 drawing, make it your own.

Look at and think about the samples. Select and choose those you like the best. If you get stuck while doing a drawing, then refer to these samples for ideas; but make the drawing your own. Being original is always best.

GA1439

Eight Shapes of Eight

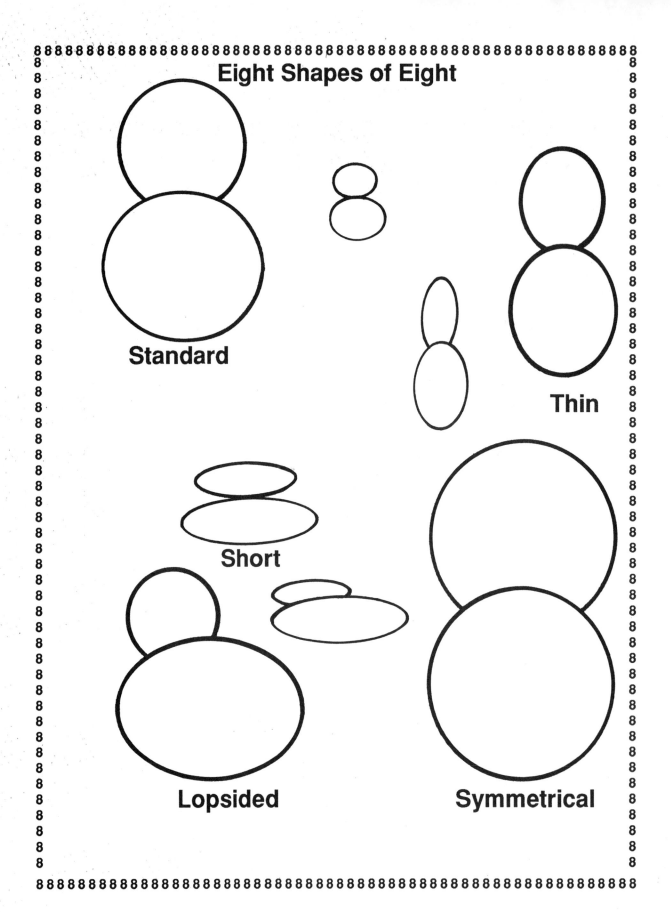

Standard

Thin

Short

Lopsided

Symmetrical

12

Eyes, Eyes and More Eyes

An eye is an arch with a pupil.

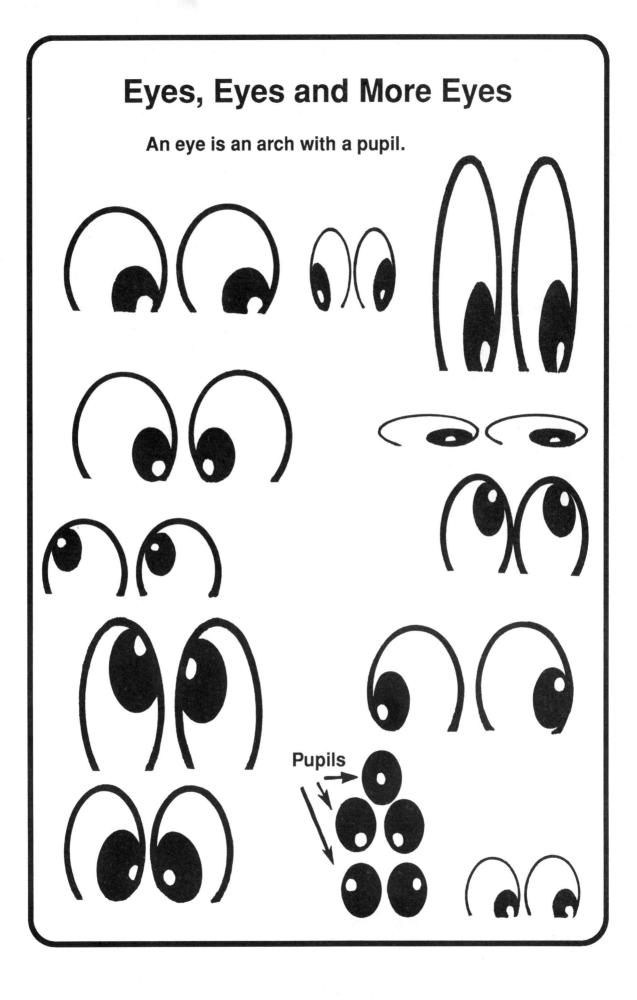

Pupils

Ears
Shapes and Sizes

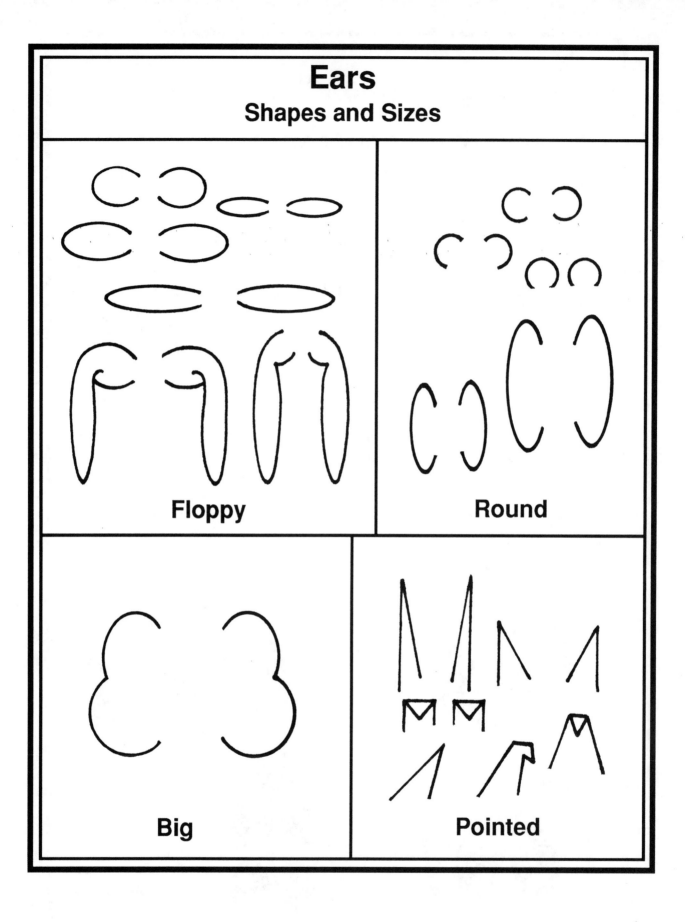

Floppy

Round

Big

Pointed

14

Noses, Mouths and Horns
A Few Samples

Nostrils for Noses

Noses   **Snout**

Mouths

Horns   **Antlers**

There are many more. Be imaginative!

CA1439

Let's Draw

"I don't know how to draw,"
Kevin Kant said.
"I can draw. I like to draw,"
Artist Artie said.

Then Susie Que
told of what she had learned to do.
By starting with a figure 8
she drew and drew and drew.

"When you start with a figure 8, "
she said, "your drawing skills improve."
"By trying, practicing and thinking about it,
I now can draw and if you try so can you."

Creativity goes
beyond
the expected!

Figure 8 drawing is something we can all do. So let's get to it!

Figure 8 drawing is fun and easy!

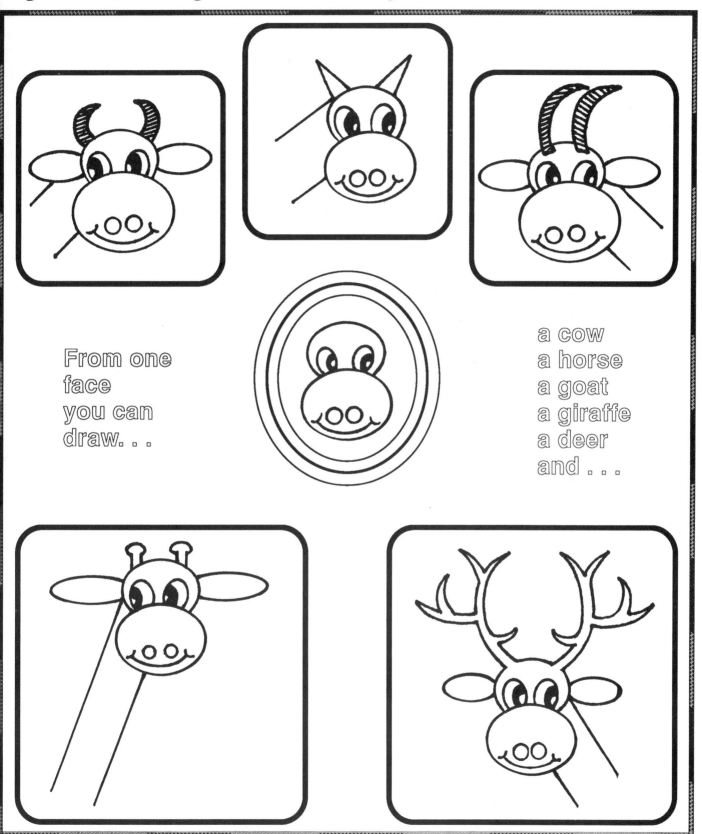

From one
face
you can
draw. . .

a cow
a horse
a goat
a giraffe
a deer
and . . .

Think of other animals to draw using this face. Try them.

17

Practice doing figure 8 drawings.

Decide what animal face you want to draw.

Think about how that face looks.

Use a pencil or crayon and trace the dotted 8.

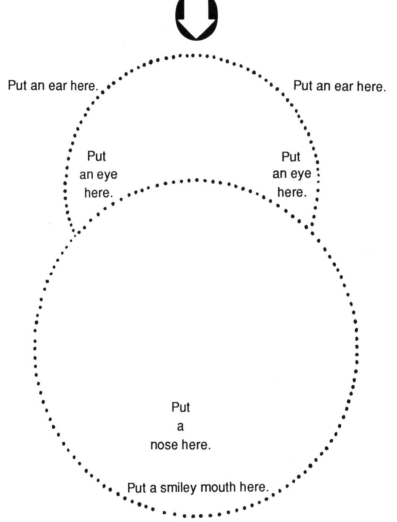

Put an ear here.　　　Put an ear here.

Put
an eye
here.　　　Put
an eye
here.

Put
a
nose here.

Put a smiley mouth here.

You may also want to add a neck, some horns and some other things.

A _____　　drawn by _____

Let's do some more.

GA1439

Here are more faces to draw.

These four figure 8's need faces. Draw them.

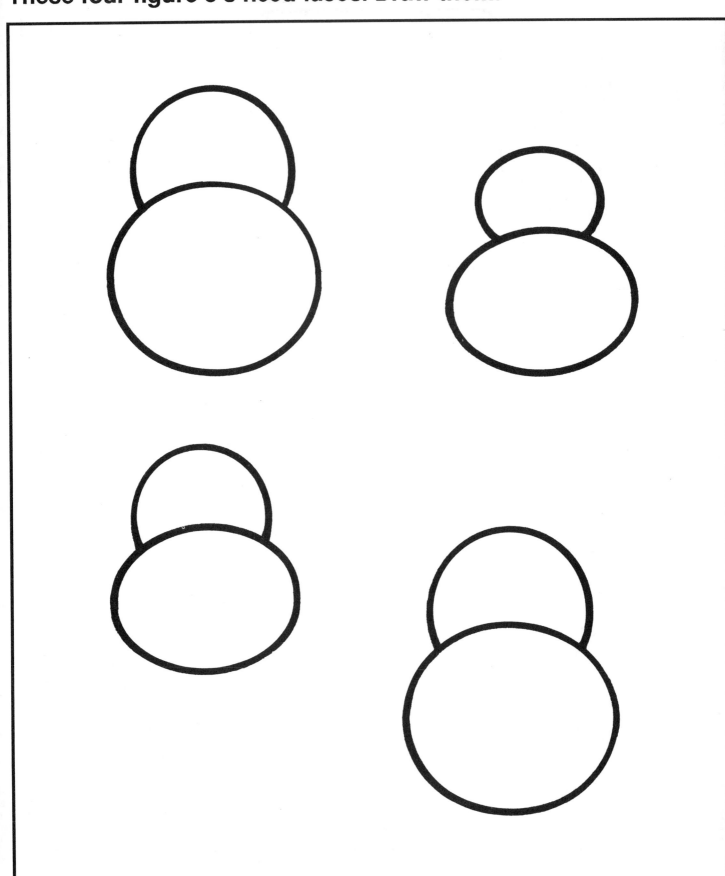

GA1439

How Do They look?

A cow looks like a cow, of course
But does a cow look like a horse?
Big eyes, long nose and mouth help a lot
The neck and ears, some horns? Maybe not.

Cows, Giraffes, Goats,
Reindeer, Elk, Moose,
Donkeys, Mules, Horses,
Dogs, Cats, Lions,
Tigers, Elephants, Hippos,
Rhinos, Pigs, Raccoons,
Armadillos, Aardvarks and Birds

Think about these animals.

How are they alike?

How are they different?

GA1439

Alike and Different

These checklists will help you compare animals.

>Choose two animals to compare.

>Write their names below.

>Using descriptive words, fill in the blanks.

1.

Animal's name _____ .

Its eyes are _____ .

Its nose is _____ .

Its nostrils are _____ .

Its ears are _____ .

Its mouth is _____ .

Its neck is _____ .

Yes or no?   If yes, describe.

Horns   ____ _____ .

Whiskers   ____ _____ .

Hair   ____ _____ .

Teeth   ____ _____ .

Other   ____ _____ .

2.

Animal's name _____ .

Its eyes are _____ .

Its nose is _____ .

Its nostrils are _____ .

Its ears are _____ .

Its mouth is _____ .

Its neck is _____ .

Yes or no?   If yes, describe.

Horns   ____ _____ .

Whiskers   ____ _____ .

Hair   ____ _____ .

Teeth   ____ _____ .

Other   ____ _____ .

In what ways are they alike?_____

_____

_____

In what ways are they different?_____

_____

_____

GA1439

Progressive Drawing

> Form groups of four to six students. In each group, each student chooses *one* part to draw. Use these lists:

    1. The figure 8   (Optional)

    2. The eyes   Neck

    3. The ears   Horns

    4. The nose   Whiskers

    5. The mouth   Tusks, fangs or teeth

Each student draws his/her part without talking.

> The figure 8 is then passed around the group, and each student in turn puts his/her part on exactly as it was drawn. At the end, a new animal will appear.

>When the drawing is complete, each group is asked to

       1. Name the animal.

       2. Determine its size.

       3. Give it a color.

       4. Describe where it might live, what it eats and some of its habits.

       5. Determine its rarity.

       6. Describe its contribution to the environment.

       Optional

       7. Establish an organization to protect it.

"A sense of humor is essential to the creative process."

GA1439

This page is for progressive drawing.

A New Animal
Drawn by

_____

_____

_____

_____

_____

Information About This Animal

Draw a picture of the new animal.

Always
start
with an
8

GA1439

Horses

25

With a ring-a-ding
and a ring-a-ding-dong
the horsemen came-a-riding
came-a-riding along

on silver white horses
shining brightly like snow
the horsemen came-a-riding
with bells a-ring-dinging every place they would go

they rode in our town
each street up and down
who they were and why they came
horses and riders without a name

ring-a-ding, ring-a-ding-dong
the years have long gone by
snow-white horses and riders came
and no one has ever known why
TC

Who do you think they were?

Why do you think they came?

What were their names?

GA1439

The Horse

and Its Family

Drawing, Imagining, Dreaming and Storytelling

Equine: The Family of Horses

Horses

Horses, as we know them, first lived wild in Europe, Asia and Africa. The only true wild horse that has survived still lives in Mongolia. There are herds of horses "wild" in the Americas. However, these were released by or escaped from early explorers and adventurers. Horses have been very important in the history of man. Before the automobile they were used for transportation and work. The horse was used to clear and cultivate land, haul heavy loads, transport goods and people and fight wars. There are now more horses than ever in the world. In some places, they are still used for work and transportation; however, many horses today are kept and used for pleasure.

Donkeys

Donkeys are a large family of animals closely related to the horse. In this family there are common donkeys, burros (tame and wild) and three distinct species of African zebras. Donkeys are smaller than horses, have larger ears, erect manes and a somewhat different tail.

Mules

Mules are unique animals. They are not a true breed. They are a hybrid of a horse and a donkey. Mules have the body of a horse and the ears, mane and tail of a donkey. They are patient, surefooted, dependable, strong animals. They are also thought to be stubborn, intelligent and very independent.

> The mule it's said is a stubborn beast.
> What you want most it wants least.

Pegasus and the Unicorn

Pegasus is an imaginary flying horse; the unicorn is a magical, beautiful horse with one horn. They live in the fantasies of our minds. They are spirits that romp and gallop through our dreams. Many tales have been and will be told about these mythical, magic horses.

GA1439

Horses, Donkeys and Mules

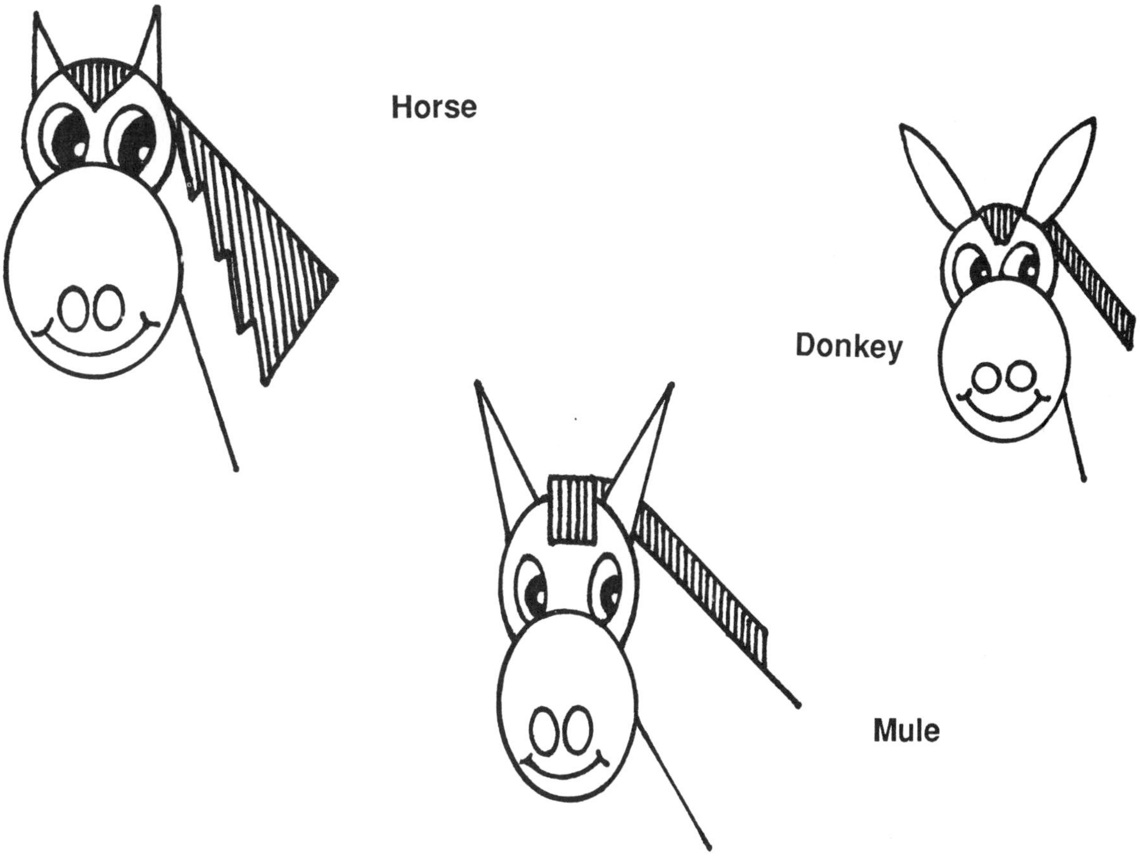

Horse

Donkey

Mule

Draw two below.

Always
start
with an

8

GA1439

Write and illustrate a story using some of the phrases below.

When	**Who**	**What**	**Where**
last year	a horse	won a prize	in a desert
long ago	a donkey	helped a friend	in a city
last weekend	a zebra	escaped	on a farm
today	a mule	returned	in the mountains
in the future	a unicorn	could talk	at school

Choose one phrase from each column.

When _____   Who _____

What _____   Where _____

Now write a story using the phrases you have chosen.

Use more paper if needed.

This page is for writing about horses or drawing horses.

GA1439

Pigs
Pigs
Pigs
Pigs
Pigs

Pigs

About Pigs

Pigs are not usually considered when a family sets out to choose a pet. They are big, heavy animals with tough skin and prickly hair. They are also noisy; they grunt, oink and squeal. They eat a lot and seem to enjoy lounging about in puddles of mud.

Pigs are members of the *suidae* family. They are closely related to the peccary (a wild pig like animal) and to the hippopotamus.

Pigs may have been one of the last wild animals to be domesticated. It seems they appeared during the sixteenth century in Europe. They apparently descended from the European wild boar. Man may have looked at the wild boar and decided that this was definitely one animal that needed to be domesticated—as a challenge. The challenge was to make it a little more attractive. Wild boars with their large heads, hairy prickly manes down the back, and fierce curved tusks on their long snouts are not very attractive. Maybe, just maybe, the ultimate challenge was to make a "pretty pig." Pigs have come a long way in terms of pretty, but I think maybe there is still some work to be done.

Did you know that pigs are trained to hunt truffles in France?

Recently, I've heard of a miniature potbellied pig that is being developed and promoted as a house pet. Some people say that they are better pets than cats or dogs. Do you think that it is possible for a pretty, potbellied pet pig to replace dogs and cats as our most popular pet?

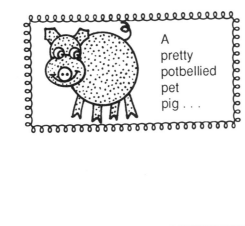

A pretty potbellied pet pig . . .

Pigs are also known as _____ and _____. *(hogs and swine)*

GA1439

Pig Projects

> Make a list of words that describe a "pretty, potbellied, pet pig." How would you disguise one?

> Read the book *Charlotte's Web* by E.B. White.

> Think of stories and rhymes about pigs. Choose one and give it a different ending.

> Interview a hog farmer.
Make a list of eight questions you would ask.
Write what you think the answers might be.
Conduct the interview and check your answers.

> Visit a supermarket and list all the items you find that are made from pigs or that contain pork (meat from pigs).

> Ask your parents and grandparents about "old sayings" that are related to pigs. What do you think they mean?

> Are there more things you would like to learn about pigs? What . . .?

Pigs are fun to draw. Some should be silly, some wacky and others with long hair, glasses and a beard. ⟶

GA1439

Pigs

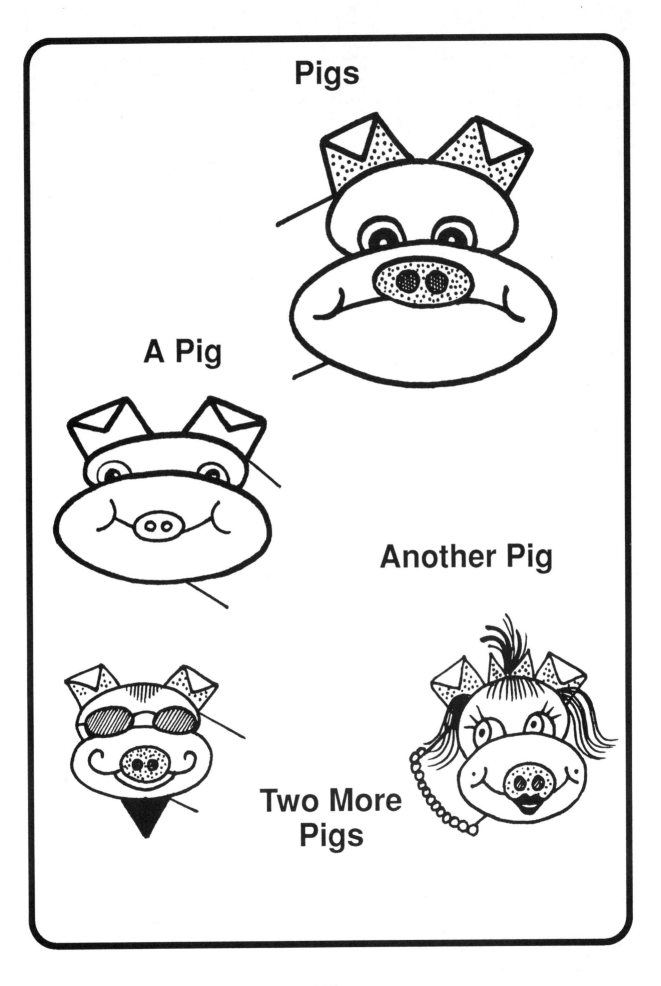

A Pig

Another Pig

Two More
Pigs

35

GA1439

This page is for drawing pigs.

Always start with an **8** → A pig 8 → A pig's little eyes → A mouth and snout → Floppy ears and a neck → And a pig is done!

Draw and describe a pretty, potbellied pet pig.

36

GA1439

This page is for four pig projects. (See page 34.)

1 _____

2 _____

3 _____

4 _____

GA1439

The Way It ~~Really~~ Happened

Really (inserted above)

On a cold and blustery night,
a dog and cat met to fight.
The cat raised his tail
and humped his back.
The dog growled and bristled
the hairs up his back.

Both stood their ground,
looked each other up and down.
Then the cat hissed
and the dog barked.
These two dreaded enemies
faced each other in the dark.

Suddenly a bright light
shattered the night.
An awful screeching sound
the silence tore.
Down upon them both
a speeding auto bore.

The cat jumped left.
The dog to the right.
They barely escaped
that car that night.

Shaking with fear
on each side of the street,
They hissed and growled
and began to retreat.

Both wisely decided
to leave the fight in the past,
each thinking he was the
one that had won at last.

TC

39

About Dogs

The wolf is thought to be the prehistoric parent of all domestic dogs. There are many kinds of wild dogs, but the wolf tends to have the closest association with man. The wolf always seems to live close to people and often depends upon them.

It is hard to imagine some of the dogs today being related to wolves. How a wolf's descendant became a Pekingese or a miniature Pomeranian is indeed a wonder. However, other dogs such as shepherds, collies and huskies certainly are wolf-like. Some of these even have a wolf's bark and stalking habits.

The first dogs to be domesticated were probably captured as puppies and kept for hunting. Since that time, dogs have been bred and raised to serve man. Some dogs are still hunters; some are workers; and many are only pets.

Dogs (hunters, workers and only pets) are known as "man's oldest, most reliable friend and companion." Many dogs have noble, almost heroic, jobs. There are Seeing Eye™ dogs for the blind. There are guard and police dogs that protect people and property. There are dogs that serve as messengers and help detect the enemy during war. Best of all, if you have a pet dog, you have a friend who likes you just the way you are.

There is much to learn about dogs. All dogs belong to the *Canidea* family and are commonly referred to as *canines*. Libraries are full of information, stories and books about dogs.

> Dog Trivia: The Dog Museum was founded in 1981 in New York City and moved to St. Louis, Missouri, in 1986. This is the only dog museum in the world.

GA1439

Figure 8 Profile Drawing

Always start with an 8

> **To do profile drawing, follow steps 1, 2, 3 and 4.**

1. Draw an 8.

2. Add some circles to the side.

3. Erase the lines you do not need.

4. Add eyes, nose, ears, mouth and neck; and your profile drawing is complete.

Many animal faces can be drawn in profile.
Some are
   dogs
   rhinos
   bears
   birds
You may think of others. Try them.

GA1439

Some Dogs

List some dogs you would like to draw.

_____   _____

_____   _____

_____   Choose some and draw them. ⟶

GA1439

This page is for drawing dogs.

Always
start
with an

8

GA1439

Activities About Dogs

Draw your favorite dog.

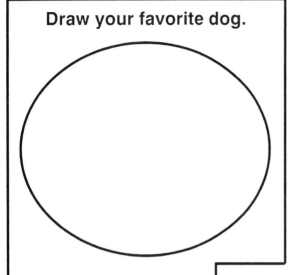

Make a list of words that describe this dog.

Create, name and describe a new breed of dog. This new dog must perform at least three different tasks.

How would you go about teaching a dog to roller-skate?

Write about what you think parents should do when a pet dies or is killed.

GA1439

c
a
t
s

45

GA1439

The Regal Cat

Cats are pets of kings and queens,
Soft, cuddly, quiet things.
Friends of kings, ladies and hobos alike,
They sleep all day, carouse all night.

Cats are pets of kings and queens,
Soft, cuddly, quiet things.
Some quietly tippytoe up on birds.
Lions roar and chase large herds.

Cats are pets of kings and queens,
Soft, cuddly, quiet things.
Pampered pets who are kept inside
Given toys, beds and places to hide.

But the most terrible thing to a mouse.
Is to have a big, mean cat in the house.

TC

Who

is

the

King?

GA1439

Cats
The Family Feline

Lions, tigers, cheetahs, cougars, bobcats and tabbies all belong to that family of independent cats. Some cats are large and ferocious; others lie in our laps and purr. Some cats can run like the wind; others plod around our houses and sleep most of the day. Some cats are famous, others are unknown. Some cats can climb trees; others prefer not. Some cats have been tamed; others have not.

Cats are interesting, intriguing and mysterious animals. The library has lots of books and stories about the wonderful and sometimes wacky cat.

More about cats.

Which cat is largest? _____ Smallest? _____

Which cat is fastest? _____ Most feared? _____

Where did cats come from? _____

_____

List characteristics all cats have in common.

_____   _____   _____

_____   _____   _____

Name three famous cats.

_____   _____   _____

Which cat would you like to have as a pet?
On the next page write and illustrate a
short story about you and a pet tiger.

GA1439

Use this page to write your story.

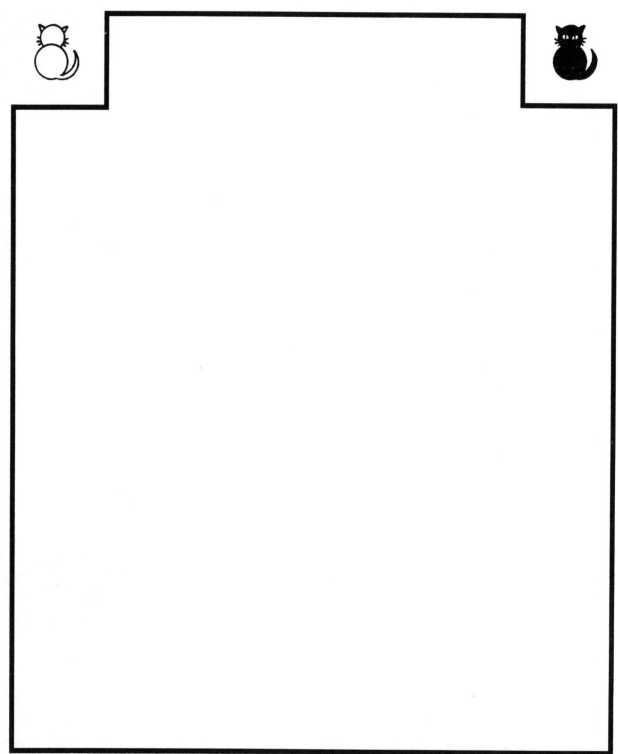

GA1439

Cats

Color them. Name them. Draw, color and name some more.

_____   _____

_____

Draw a cat here.

To draw a cat, start with an 8 upside down.

Then finish the cat's face.

Draw a cat here.

Finish this sentence: Cats are _____, _____

and _____.

49

GA1439

Cat Faces

Remember: To draw a cat face,
start with an upside down 8.

Figure 8 Cat Silhouettes

Try them!

GA1439

Activities About Cats

Draw three funny cat faces.

Write a poem about a cat, bat, mat and _____ .

List and briefly describe five different kinds of cats.

Write a story about a stowaway cat on a space shuttle.

Report on a famous cat. (comic, cartoon or real)

Design, draw and describe a unique house for a cat.

Tell how you would teach a cat two new tricks.

Choose two activities and do them below.

Activity 1	Activity 2

GA1439

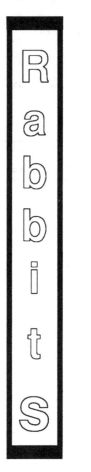

Rabbits

Rabbits

Rabbits

Rabbits

Rabbits

Rabbits

and Hares

GA1439

Rabbits and Hares

Bugs Bunny is the most famous rabbit I know. He is a cunning and mischievous fellow. It seems that trouble follows him; no one ever really likes him; and usually, he is somewhere he should not be. But regardless of the problem, he finds a way out and usually wins.

Bugs Bunny is not a typical rabbit. Neither is Peter Cotton Tail nor Brer Rabbit. However, the one thing they all have in common with other rabbits is that they are pesky and generally disliked.

Rabbits and hares are of the *Leporidae* family, closely related to rodents. They live just about everywhere on Earth. If they were not native to a country, they were imported as a valuable resource of food and fur. There are several species of rabbits. Some are relatively large and others quite small. Some species are threatened with extinction while others flourish or have overpopulated. They are an important link in the food chain for larger predators like hawks, eagles, foxes, wolves and wild cats.

There are some strange facts about imported rabbits and their effect on the ecology of Australia. You may be interested in learning about this.

GA1439

Rabbits and Hares

And "Rare-bits" to Do
> Use the figure 8 to draw some unique rabbits.
> Write a poem starting with "If a rabbit had wings to fly . . . ."
  Rhyming words you might use–*sky, high, sigh, by* (list more).
> Learn more about rabbits.
> Read stories about rabbits.
> Write a story about a rabbit family, a fox, a secret hiding place and a very big, very friendly dog.

Do you know how to catch a "unique-wabbit"?
"You-neak" up on it.

GA1439

This page is for thinking about and drawing rabbits.

Finish drawing this rabbit then draw some more.

55

GA1439

This page is for writing rabbit stories or writing about rabbits.

56

More Drawing Ideas

Silhouettes and Outlines
with figure 8's

Creativity goes
beyond
the expected!

57

GA1439

Animal
Adventures
Continue

GA1439

Giraffes

Draw a giraffe here.

The words that best describe a giraffe are *long* and *tall*. Giraffes have long front legs and longer necks. Together these make them very tall. Most giraffes live wild in Africa, but it seems that every zoo has giraffes.

Giraffes are browsers—they eat mostly leaves from trees. Their long front legs and longer necks are really helpful for this. When they eat grass or drink water, they either kneel or spread their front legs so wide that they look as though they may disassemble themselves.

Giraffes are large animals. Actually the giraffe is the tallest of all animals. Some males reach nearly 20 feet tall and weigh nearly 2000 pounds. The females are somewhat smaller.

Do you know any other interesting facts about giraffes?

Where could you learn more about giraffes?

Can you think of three places?

GA1439

My Story
The Day Gina the Gentle Giraffe Met Geoff

By _____

These ideas may help you with your story.

When	Where	What	Who is Geoff?
last weekend	the zoo	got in trouble	a giraffe
yesterday	a circus	ran away	a boy
today	a school	became heroes	a man
the Fourth of July	a mall	made the team	another animal

Think of others.

60

GA1439

A Giraffe in a Glass Carafe

A decree went out all over the land
the king was offering rewards for
birds in the hand.

fishes in dishes
turtles in bottles
a dog on a log
a frog in a bog
a fat cat on a mat
a how now brown cow
and a giraffe
in a glass carafe

The king's servants said
they had found them all.

fishes in dishes
turtles in bottles
a dog on a log
a frog in a bog
a fat cat on a mat
a how now brown cow

But, alas
a giraffe in a glass carafe
had not been found at all!

TC

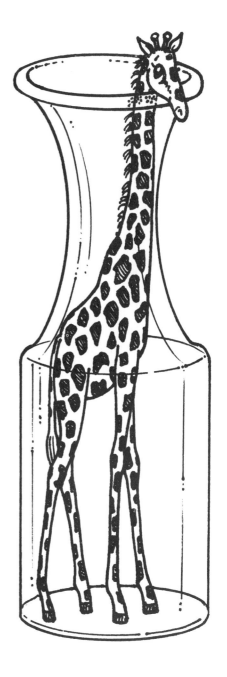

Design and draw a device which will put the giraffe in the carafe.

The device must have at least three different working parts and not harm the giraffe.

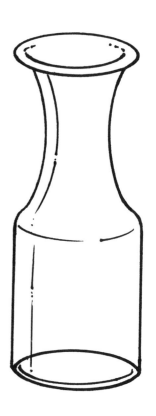

62

GA1439

Hippos

and

Rhinos

GA1439

Hipporhinomi
About Hippos and Rhinos

Hippopotamus
Hippopotamus amphibius
Hippos are from Africa. They live mostly in water and eat amphibious vegetation. Hippos have four toes, are about five feet tall and weigh almost four tons. They also sunburn easily.

If you had a hippopotamus for a pet, where would you keep it?

Rhinoceros
Rhinoceros unicornis
Rhinos also live in Africa. They eat grass and plants. Rhinos have three toes, a valuable horn on their nose, and are about the same size as hippopotami.

How would you describe a ride on a rhinoceros?

On the next page write and illustrate a story about
>"Harry the Hip Hippo Visits Grandmother" or
>"Riding Rena the Regal Rhino to a Restaurant"

My Story

Title: _____

Written and illustrated by _____

Draw a hippopotamus or two.

Always
start
with an
8

Draw a rhinoceros or two.

Draw a hipporhinomus wearing sunglasses.

GA1439

This page is for listing.

*List things that would make a hippopotamus hyperventilate.

_____

_____

_____

_____

_____

_____

_____

_____

_____

_____

List ways to elevate an elephant.

_____

_____

_____

_____

_____

_____

_____

_____

_____

_____

_____

_____

List things that would make an alligator angry.

_____

_____

_____

_____

_____

_____

_____

_____

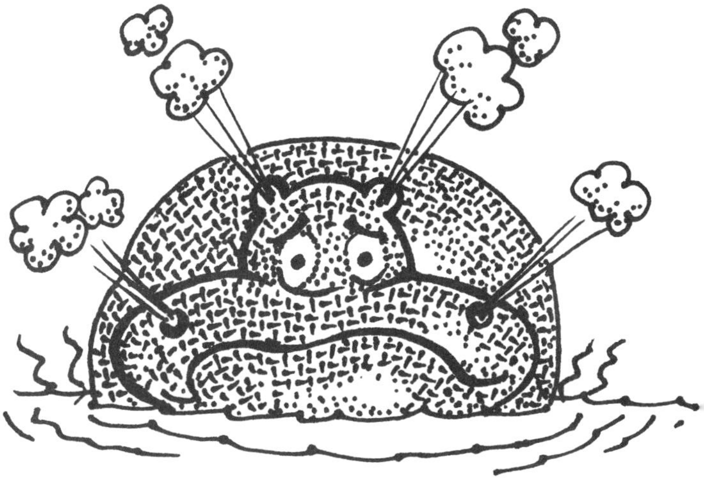

_____

*The "hyperventilating hippopotamus" from Bob Stanish's book *Hippogriff Feathers*, Good Apple, Inc., 1981.

GA1439

Elephants

68

GA1439

About Elephants

Whales are the largest mammals on Earth, but they live in the ocean. Elephants are the largest of all land animals. There are two kinds of elephants, the Asiatic and the African. The easiest way to tell them apart is to look at their ears. The African elephant's ears are much larger than Asiatic elephant's ears. The Asiatic elephant is also smaller than the African elephant, but for most of us this would be hard to tell because both are very large. Counting the toes is another way to tell them apart. One has only three toes on its hind feet, the other has four.

An elephant's nose is stretched into a trunk. The trunk is used for more than breathing. It is used for putting water and food in the elephant's mouth, smelling for danger and lifting or moving things.

Elephants are easily trained and have been used for work and transportation for thousands of years.

It's said that an elephant cannot jump, but when you are as big as an elephant why would you need to or want to?

The mastodon, the elephant's ancient relative, once roamed over most of the earth. It was a large, hairy, long tusked, big eared animal that looked very much like today's elephant.

A Lighterthanairaphant

GA1439

Elephants Are for Fun

face

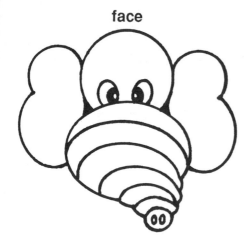

body

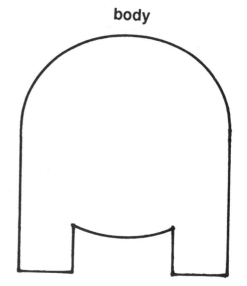

front view

side view

What is this?

Always start with an **8**

70

This page is for drawing or writing about elephants.

71

the tiny elephant

imagine an elephant
as small as an ant
imagine an elephant being so smug
as to be as small as a bug
and hide in the rug
under Zach's miniature toy tug

the ant elephant pretends
the tug captain to be
he's so small so hard to see
tiny elephant bug under Zach's miniature tug
smack dab in the middle of the rug
the elephant believes that rug
a vast and stormy sea to be
and captain of that mighty tug
the tiny elephant pretends to be

he climbs aboard Zach's capsized tug
with his trunk he grabs a hair of the rug
gives the hair a heave and a tug
and with a final heave and a tug
he turns upright Zach's miniature tug
and singing a salty sea song
he cheerfully sails along
on the sea on the rug

ant elephants
tiny tug captains
and stormy rug seas
are these all impossibilities?

not if you imagine
and see what I see
not if you pretend
and daydream like me

TC

Some exciting elephant activities are on the next page.

GA1439

Elephant Activities

List some places a very small elephant could hide.

Elephants are very intelligent. If an elephant were in control of the world, what could it do to make the world better?

Write an elephant joke.

Name five different things that together would balance this elephant.

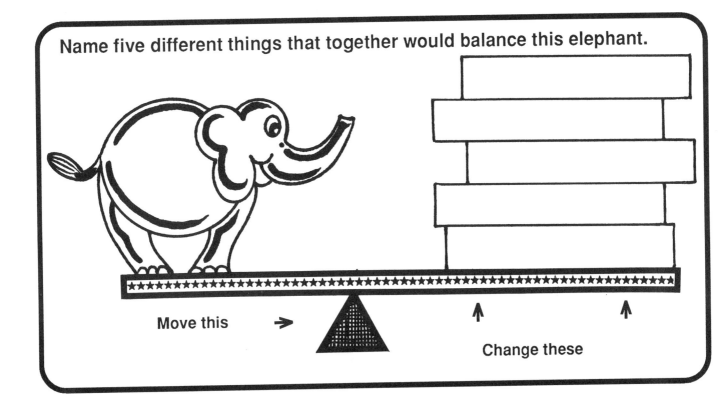

Move this →

Change these

Anteaters

Aardvarks

Armadillos

Anteaters

The family of anteaters is a group of unrelated animals that, guess what, eat ants. There are several anteaters that live in South America. They all have long faces, tubular snouts and long, sticky tongues. The largest is about four feet long, has long hair and a long bushy tail. Anteaters also have powerful front legs and claws that they use to defend themselves and to dig up their favorite food: ants, termites and small insects.

GA1439

Aardvarks

Aardvarks live in Africa, eat ants, sleep during the day, hunt at night and defend themselves by burrowing quickly underground. They look somewhat like a pig because of their long snouts, little mouths and little eyes. The aardvarks ears are long, roundish and fit squarely on top of their heads.

They have an interesting family name that you may want to "look up."

Armadillos

Armadillos live in the tropical Americas. Recently their range has expanded creating a population explosion of armadillos in the southwestern United States. The armadillo has an armor-like skin covering its head and body. (That may be why it is called *arma*dillo.) Armadillos eat bugs, worms and fruit. There are several different kinds and sizes of armadillos. You may want to learn more about this intriguing animal, or maybe not.

More Anteaters, Aardvarks and Armadillos

Aardvarks and armadillos are together because of the way it sounds when you say *aaarrrdvark* and *aar-rmadillo*.

Things to Do

- Practice saying *aaarrrdvark* and *aarrmadillo* as though you are surprised, confused, delighted, frightened, very fond of and disgusted.

- Draw anteaters, aardvarks and armadillos using the figure 8.

- Write a report on anteaters, aardvarks or armadillos.

- Have a debate about
  >Which came first, the aardvark or the armadillo?
  >Which would make the best pet, an aardvark or an armadillo?

- Write a letter to your favorite.
  >Aaron Aardvark, a rock music star
  >Admire Armadillo, the most beautiful girl in the movies

- See next page.

GA1439

Bird Curiosities

Some birds fly, others cannot.
Some birds swim, others will not.
Some live near water, others do not.
Some birds live in cold, others in hot.
Some like it neither too cold nor too hot.
Birds migrate north, south, east and west.
Spending each season where they like best.

Some birds fly only at night.
Others fly only at day.
A bat, at night, looks like a bird,
but it's not, it just looks that way.

There are birds as big as a man,
others will fit in the palm of your hand.
Remember, for each bird you see,
that bird an egg used to be.
When birds soar in the sky
and look down on you and me,
Do you wonder if they think,
"Without us, what would this world be?"

81

GA1439

Birds of All Kinds

There are millions of birds.
There are sparrows, robins, blackbirds,
blue jays, seagulls, doves, pigeons and wrens.
On the farm, you will find turkeys, ducks, geese
and chickens—both roosters and hens.
Let's draw some birds. Here's how it begins.

First draw a figure 8, of course.

Note: The 8 is extended by a neck.

either 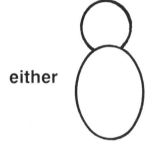 or  or

Then think about a bird.

There are many choices.

Jan Barry helped
me draw this
parrot.

You draw some birds.

*From Jan Barry's book *Draw, Design and Paint*, Good Apple, Inc., 1990

More Birds

plain

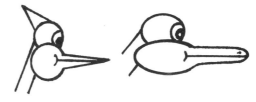

and fancy

flying, too!

83

GA1439

Draw some birds plain and fancy.

Plain

Fancy

84

Bird Things to Do

>Draw some birds
　　or a tree with birds
　　　　or a picture with a big sky and birds.

>Read books or stories about birds.

>Write a story that includes
　　you, a bird, a trip
　　　　and a wizard.

>Have a campaign and elect a class bird.

>Find bird records:
　　largest, smallest,
　　　　fastest, etc.

>Give a report about your favorite bird.

>Choose a pet bird. Tell
　　why you chose it,
　　　　how to care for it,
　　　　　　where to keep it.

>Think about what an Archeaopteryx could be.

>Read the book *Jonathan Livingston Seagull* by Richard Bach.

GA1439

GA1439

Alien 8's

An alien 8 is strange, different or unfamiliar. To draw alien 8's, use your imagination. Think strange and unusual. Draw your thoughts.

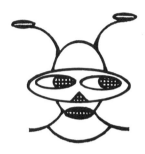

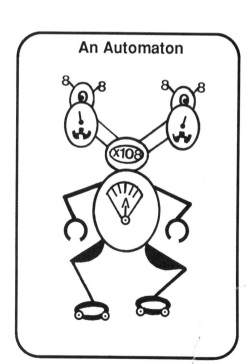

An Automaton

Always
start
with an
8

87

GA1439

I challenge you dreamers to be
    to wonder about
        the birds in the sky
           the fish in the sea
              the animals of Earth
                all the creatures you see

I challenge you dreamers to be
    especially to wonder
        about you and me
           we need each other to ask and explore
           our questions
              our dreams
                and our curiosities

GA1439

It all

started

with an 8.

89

References and Suggested Readings

Bach, Richard. *Jonathan Livingston Seagull*. New York: Avon Books, 1970.

Barry, Jan. *Draw, Design and Paint*. Carthage, Illinois: Good Apple, Inc., 1990.

Cole, Troy. "Minute Minders." *Challenge*, 1990-1992, Vol. 9 (1)-Vol. 10 (5).

Eberle, Bob. *Scamper: Games for Imagination Development*. Buffalo, New York: D.O.K. Publishers, 1971.

Eberle, Bob, and Bob Stanish. *CPS for Kids: A Resource Book for Teaching Creative Problem Solving to Children*. Buffalo, New York: D.O.K. Publishers, 1980.

Raths, Louis E., Merrill Harmin, and Sidney B. Simon. *Values and Teaching*. rev. ed. Columbus, Ohio: Charles E. Merrill Publishing Co., 1977.

Saint-Exupery, Antoine de. *The Little Prince*. New York: Harcourt, Brace & World, 1943.

Stanish, Bob. *Ac'cents and Ascendings*. Carthage, Illinois: Good Apple, Inc., 1990.

Stanish, Bob. *Connecting Rainbows*. Carthage, Illinois: Good Apple, Inc., 1982.

Stanish, Bob. *The Giving Book: Creative Classroom Approaches to Caring, Valuing and Cooperating*, Carthage, Illinois: Good Apple, Inc., 1988.

Stanish, Bob. *Hippogriff Feathers: Encounters with Creative Thinking*. Carthage, Illinois: Good Apple, Inc., 1981.

Stanish, Bob. *Mindanderings*. Carthage, Illinois: Good Apple, Inc., 1990.

Stanish, Bob. *Sunflowering*. Carthage, Illinois: Good Apple Inc., 1986.

White E.B. *Charlotte's Web*.

GA1439

j   Cole, Troy W.
372.5   Figure 8 Animals
Col

DATE DUE

AP 1 6 '94		

Demco, Inc. 38-293